The Wind and the Rain

Simon & Schuster, New York

The Wind and the Rain

CHILDREN'S POEMS

Collected by Richard Lewis/Photographs by Helen Buttfield

First Printing

Library of Congress Catalog Card Number: 68-18331
Manufactured in the United States of America; printed by Sanders Printing Corp.,
New York, N.Y.; bound by Edition Book Bindery, Clifton, N.J.

THE WIND AND THE RAIN brings together poetry written by children with photographs by Helen Buttfield. Some of the poems are taken from *Miracles*, while others are being published here for the first time.

Between the poetry and the photographs we have explored, through the images created by the poet and photographer, the moods, sensations, and ideas experienced in our relationship with some aspects of the natural world. The photographs are meant to be not so much interpretations of the poems as complements to them—bringing into sharper focus the poetical sense of nature these children, and children everywhere, express through their words.

R.L.

H.B.

Lying in the sun
In Midsummer
Looking at a blue sheet
Of happiness.
Only a breath of wind
To spoil it.

Ian Johnson
Age 9

The trees share their shade with
all who pass by,
But their leaves whisper secrets
only to the wind.

Nelda Dishman
Age 12

Wrinkles run down the pool,
As white silvery water pours down.
The sunshine makes it colorful.
Then the calm breeze goes by letting
The grass sing with the wind too.
As birds stay still for a minute
And listen to the trees shake.

Reg Cowie
Age 8

The wind is like the yeast in bread.
It makes the clouds fluffy white, not red.
It bakes them in the oven of the sky,
Then sets them loose. I wonder why?

Robert Tanaka
Age 11

Soiled clouds hang,
A clap of thunder booms
Afar.
The air is hotly still;
Not a breath of wind and
We are restless.

A tree stands,
The monarch of the field,
Moving not a leaf.
Suddenly
The electricity of the sky
Flashes
And lets us glimpse
The counterpane of earth.
Clouds gather in a conference,
And then the welcome rain
Comes pattering.

Susan Meader
Age 10

16

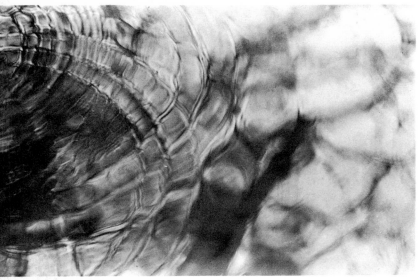

Slowly slowly the drip drip drop
Splick splick . . . splock of coming rain
And then the roar

As icily cold needles penetrate
    the skin of things
To the very very cold bone core.

Jennifer Lloyd
Age 13

See this beautiful rainy day
That waters the pretty flowers,
And washes away my hopscotch.

Alliene Graver
Age 7

19

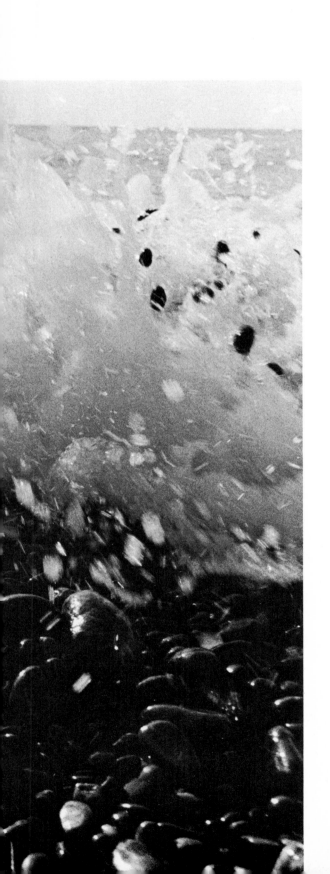

A storm at sea is dangerous.
The wind blows as if it had no
      sympathy.
The sky suddenly darkens—
A slash of lightning crosses
      the sky.
Then a sound like a giant
Stamping his feet
      in anger.
A spray of tiny stars would
      come from the waves...
Huge blue-green hands
      with white fingers
Rise from the sea.

Delia Valentin
Age 10

21

Raindrops shimmer down dirty glass
And measle the windowpane.
The raindrops glide—leaving a motionless road.
Raindrops fall, breaking themselves to tiny china,
and run away like blood.

Ken Dickinson
Age 10

What a terrible day.
Too wet to play,
Bored stiff,
Nothing to do.
Look out the window.
Big black clouds

Stream in flood,
Cars flash by,
No sun.
Nothing to hear
But the drip, drip, drop of rain.

Barry Ovens
Age 10

Many shiver
        in their bed.
                A heavy rain
                        A wet rose.

Jocelyn Klein
Age 11

It is a night of milky clouds;
Moon-blue cloud.
It is a night of wind and street-lights.
Everything is asleep.
Darkness: a grave of clouds,
Rain, hail, a wet cat meowing,
Me, a moth, and night.

Shirley Gash
Age 10

The pattering rain dances
Like a lovely maiden
Waltzing in the wind.
Blithe breezes stroke their harps,
As clouds leap in step with misty partners,
Trying to embrace the thirsty earth.

Barbara Krasnoff
Age 9

Wind whining a lonely sound,
Wind swaying till it touches
        the ground.

Judy Evans
Age 8

Grass looks like thousands of little green elves
All running the same way.

Susan Pilkington
Age 10

Ride the four winds
Ride the four winds gallantly,
Whistling there in hymns.
Ride the four horses
Ride the four winds bravely,
Snap the blossoms from their reach
Hanging on the old peach tree.
Ride the four horses
Ride the four winds.

Shirley Gash
Age 10

Cold snuggle.
Not a sound.
Cold struck its woven webbed bed
Which curled round and round.

Cold struck its cornered bed.
Night covered in darkness
Black.
Buzzing insects struck its webbed bed.

But too cold for the helpless spider
He sat there
Not a move
Thin-sticked legs shut away.

Raindrops fell
The night grew colder.

Jennifer Lloyd
Age 13

The wind is half the flower
Because it is in the flower.
The white flower is in the clouds.

Diane Cairns
Age 10

Wind is a world without end.

Alan Hall
Age 9

34

The sun tries to reach the dark shore.

Maria Ware
Age 9

The North Wind cries aloud
As it whistles through the trees
And through the mountain peaks,
As it finally drowns in an echo.

Lisa Weg
Age 10

When you walk against the wind
You feel like a groper
Pushing its way through the strong currents
Of the sea.

Jeffrey Kemp
Age 8

41

The clouds go over the sun
To a new day.

Puti
Age 5

ACKNOWLEDGMENTS

The editor would like to thank Alistair Campbell, without whom the concept of this book could not have originated; Elwyn Richardson, for his concern for the creative work of children and for generously making seven poems from his own manuscript material available for this publication; Janet Chenery and Anne Stephenson for their editorial acumen; and all the children whose poems appear in this book for the beauty they have passed on to us through their words.

Selections from this book have been published previously in school publications of the Tawa School, Wellington, New Zealand, and the Hay Park School, Mt. Roskill, New Zealand; in an earlier version of *The Wind and the Rain*, edited by Richard Lewis, with photographs by Helen Buttfield, printed and distributed by the School Publications Branch, Department of Education, Wellington, New Zealand; and in *Miracles*, copyright © 1966 by Richard Lewis, published by Simon and Schuster. "Cold Snuggle" is reprinted from Elwyn Richardson's anthology *In the Early World*, copyright © 1964 by the New Zealand Council for Educational Research, and is used with the kind permission of the Council and Mr. Richardson.

Date Due

MAY 12 '69	MR 27 '74	APR 13 '79	APR 2 7 1998		
JUL 27 '69	AP 8 '74	OCT 2 2 '79	NOV 0 3 1998		
OCT 1 6 '69	MR 25 '75	FEB 14 '80	DEC 0 1 1998		
OC 31 '69	AP 21 '76	DEC 2 2 '8	OCT 3 1 2002		
NO 1 4 '69	DE 21 '76	OCT 0 6 1982			
JY 3 0 '70	MAR 3 '77	NOV 20 '84			
FEB 16 '71	DEC 19 '77	DEC 3 '84			
OCT 5 '71	MAR 16 '78	FACULTY			
MR 30 '73	MAR 1 8 '79	FACULTY			

PRINTED IN U.S.A. CAT. NO. 23231